Glory Be!

Charleston, SC
www.PalmettoPublishing.com

Glory Be!
Copyright © 2022 by Veronica Jaeger O'Sullivan

Photos by: Sarah Christene Bass

First Edition

Hardcover ISBN: 979-8-8229-0832-1
Paperback ISBN: 979-8-8229-0833-8

Glory Be!

Veronica Jaeger O'Sullivan

Photos by Sarah Christene Bass

As the autumn sun began to set over the farm and the cool evening air brought a chill, a farmer closed her kitchen window.

She did not notice that something small and black had fallen from a leaf and nestled into the dirt of the flower box.

A chrysalis, slightly wrinkled, rested against the window ledge.

When the sun rose the next morning and the rooster began to crow, the farmer opened the window and inhaled the crisp, fresh air.

In place of the hidden chrysalis, a bright-orange monarch butterfly had emerged.

Surprised to see this vivid splash of color, the farmer took a closer look at the shivering butterfly.

The farmer watched as the butterfly slowly crawled to the top of a leaf and began fluttering its wings, allowing the cool breeze to dry them.

The farmer noticed that, despite fluttering for quite some time, the ends of its wings, which had been wrinkled inside the fallen chrysalis, would not unfurl.

"Glory be!" exclaimed the farmer. "Your wings have not fully formed. How will you fly away? Will you let me help you? I will name you Glory."

Each day the farmer mixed some honey water for Glory to drink. The butterfly's tiny tongue, called a proboscis, worked like a little straw, drinking the liquid and gaining energy.

The farmer let Glory climb on her hands while waving its wings to make them strong.

On day four, the
farmer worried
because Glory would
not drink nor would
it flutter.

Would this butterfly
ever be strong
enough to fly
free? The farmer
whispered a tiny
prayer.

Miraculously,
by the next
day, and every
day after,
Glory drank
the honey water
and flapped its
beautiful wings.

The monarch grew stronger
and began to take short
flights, landing gently
between the houseplants
and the farmer's hands...
and her head!

One morning, as the sunlight beamed through the window onto Glory's shimmering body, the farmer knew it was time to set Glory free.

Even with its wrinkled wings, this monarch was one of God's perfect creations, specially designed for a purpose in this magical and mysterious world.

That afternoon, the farmer carried Glory to a large shrub and rested its delicate body upon a soft, pink blossom.

Ever so slowly, the wrinkled wings caught a gentle breeze.

Glory was lifted up to the sky.

As the farmer looked out through her window, her eyes
squinting into the sunlight, a small, happy
tear fell from her cheek and nestled
into the dirt of the flower box.

This book about Glory the monarch butterfly is based on <u>two</u> real-life stories.

Glory's chrysalis was discovered by my friend and former teacher, Sarah Christene Bass. Mrs. Bass was my teacher in both second and fifth grade and inspired me to have an absolute sense of wonder in the world. She continues to inspire and teach me new things to this day. Mrs. Bass nurtured Glory for twelve days, in the fall of 2022, until she set him[1] free. The photos in this book are of Glory.

---

1   We know Glory was a male butterfly because of the two black dots seen in the veins of his hind wings. (photo)

The second real-life story is that of my friend Lisa Manyata Olson. Lisa was born in India with a physical difference. She was born without arms or legs. At only a few days old, a very caring doctor brought Lisa to a children's home. The loving nurses at the children's home located a very special American woman named Marie Olson who wanted to adopt Lisa. At age five, Lisa was adopted and came to live with her mother in New York. The doctor, the nurses, and her mother, Marie, all played a part in helping Lisa become a strong and capable woman.

Due to Lisa's physical differences, she has depended on caregivers to assist her with the

daily tasks most of us take for granted, such as showering, getting dressed, hairstyling, and driving to work. Proceeds from the sale of this book will go toward the cost of daily care for Lisa and people like her.

Perhaps you know someone with a physical difference. Is there something you can offer to do that will be helpful?

Remember not all differences can be seen on the outside. Everyone needs our help from time to time.

Day One:

Today, I was given a most miraculously stunning gift. This morning, I couldn't believe my eyes! This huge monarch had emerged from its tiny capsule! It lay on its back, and I realized it had to be free for its wings to dry. I took it outside where it stayed to dry out. Its wings were a bit dark and rumpled from newborn moisture. In absolute awe, I watched it.

—Written by Sarah Christene Bass
on September 18, 2022

Freedom Day:

The weather had been glorious these past few days, and I had seen several monarchs still flitting about. I decided that, whatever Glory's fate was to be, I wanted him to experience it in freedom. I fed him one last time, and he ate well. By the end of the day, Glory had flown away.

What an incredible gift Glory has given us these past few days. I thought to myself, "If I knew, at my birth, that I would only live a few days, but those days would bring joy, awe, wonder, and learning to so many, it would have been a life richly lived." Amen.

—Written by Sarah Christene Bass on October 1, 2022

Lisa founded Manyata Ministries.

Lisa's birth name, Manyata, means "acceptance."
Manyata Ministries is a nonprofit organization that seeks
to spread the word of God's love and acceptance to all.

If you would like to learn more about Lisa, or make a tax-
deductible donation to Manyata Ministries, please visit:
www.weatherthestorms.org

"I praise you because I am
fearfully and wonderfully made;
your works are wonderful,
I know that full well."
Psalm 139:14

About the Author

Veronica Jaeger O'Sullivan was born and raised in the Hudson Valley of New York. With the Appalachian Trail running through the woods behind her childhood home, Veronica grew up with a love for exploring nature. Lisa and Veronica's friendship began in the third grade.

Veronica is a sociologist who continues to be curious about individuals, their environment, and the interdependent communities that evolve as a result of the influence each has on the other. Veronica believes that the relationships that exist in nature are mirrored in society; however, humans have the opportunity to think critically and freely choose a path that aligns with an indescribable desire to fulfill a God-given purpose.

After an accomplished career in the legal-services industry, Veronica is pursuing her purpose along a new creative path. She hopes that you, too, will make choices that allow you to fulfill God's dream for your life.

Veronica lives in sunny South Carolina and enjoys year-round walks on the beach with her husband, David, and their son, Hunter.

CPSIA information can be obtained
at www.ICGtesting.com
Printed in the USA
BVHW011913160223
658686BV00001B/7